SIX TASTES

the ayurvedic route to food health

living younger longer

CLARE BERRY

Recipes / Chef Clare Berry
Illustrations & Design Olivia Sims
Photography Chris Berry

Published by Pudding Publishing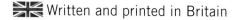
Copyright © Clare Berry 2015

Written and printed in Britain

www.sixtastesayurveda.com

Printed and bound by CPI Group (UK) Ltd, Croydon, CRO 4YY

This book is dedicated to Chris, Sassy and Olly
who mean the world to me.

I am hugely grateful to my family and friends for their tireless patience and enthusiasm and for acting as invaluable, and mostly willing, test subjects for me to test my Ayurvedic recipes on.

I cannot express how much I love Chris, my husband, for all the encouragement and support he has given me, right from the beginning of this project. I am also extremely grateful to him for his fantastic photography.

Two other people without whom this book would never have been written are Olivia Sims and Dr Mani from Mauritius. Olivia for all her beautiful watercolour illustrations and stunning book design, and Dr Mani who first sparked my interest and educated me in Ayurveda.

CONTENTS

WELCOME

'To eat is a necessity, but to eat intelligently is an art'
La Rochefoucauld

Seven years ago I had never heard of the word Ayurveda, let alone understood it.
Now I am convinced of its benefits as a completely new approach to cooking, for overall
super-charged health, both physically and mentally.

It has taken me years to write this book but during that time I have developed a passion
for it, testing out my recipes on my family, to make sure they all believed it was worth
doing. They have all vouched for the beneficial effect of the recipes on their energy, mood
and immediate feeling of well-being, after eating just one of my home-made Ayurvedic
creations. Good food, good mood!

This book aims to re-awaken your senses, in every way, and show you a totally fresh and
beneficial approach to cooking. It is an introduction to one of the most fundamental
concepts of Ayurvedic cooking: balancing all six tastes, at once on your tongue, in every
meal. The six tastes are salty, sweet, sour, bitter, astringent, pungent. Balancing all six

should prevent food cravings and promote faster digestion and appetite satiation, leading to huge health benefits. All my recipes are easy to cook, incredibly light and healthy, and leave you feeling fuller for longer.

Two of the biggest current health issues are obesity and diabetes which are caused, in part, by over-eating of processed foods. Our bodies lose the ability to tell our brain when we feel full and satiated. I have found it is clear that our body does reach a point of satiation when it receives balanced nutrition. My recipes will hopefully prove to you that we can feel full and rejuvenated on much less food than we are eating at the moment.

My dishes will give you a surge of energy, make you eat less and leave you with a sense of well-being and healthiness, even if you only make them once in a while. Food is one of the main things that we can control that we put into our bodies, which has a major effect on our both our health and mind. There is an old adage that we are what we eat, and yet we seem to be abusing that in the way we eat today.

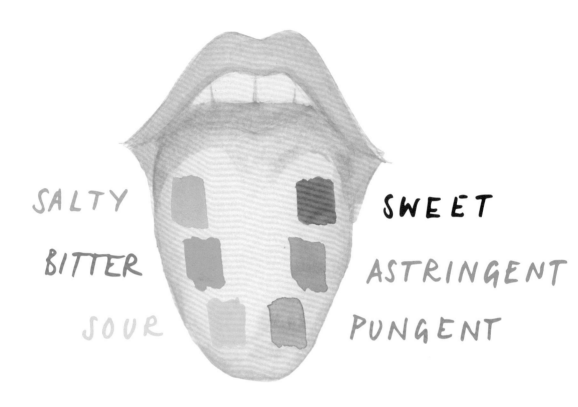

SALTY

SWEET

BITTER

ASTRINGENT

SOUR

PUNGENT

This tongue map is for illustrative purposes, tastes are actually detected all over the tongue.

THE SIX TASTES

Ayurveda teaches us that we can detect six distinct tastes on our tongue: sweet, sour, salty, bitter, pungent and astringent. Although in the West it is believed there are only five tastes: sweet, sour, salty, bitter and umami.

The tongue is covered with papillae (the small pink bumps) and taste buds that sense the six tastes. The taste buds are located all over the tongue. As we savour food on our tongues, the taste receptors send messages to the rest of our body to signal an immediate response. Signals are sent to the brain to tell the stomach enzymes to get ready for the food that is on its way down to be digested.

There are specific enzymes and hormones responsible for the different food tastes. So if you eat a salty crisp, the tongue sends a message to the brain that tells the enzymes responsible for digesting salty food, to get ready for action. These enzymes fill the stomach and intestine in preparation to digest the salty food on its way down, so it can be absorbed into the blood stream and our organs. If you only savour one or two tastes at a time, the enzymes responsible for digesting that type of food become over-dominant. They are out of balance and 'scream' for more of that taste, which is why you crave more saltiness, after eating just one crisp, whereas if you hadn't eaten one, you wouldn't even be thinking of salt let alone craving more of it. The same goes for a sweet.

Indulging these cravings leads to more of the specific enzymes being produced and creates a vicious circle, with the effect that we never feel satiated. Not only that, but these out-of-balance enzymes are then left in unnatural volumes that they wouldn't normally be in. They then build up *'ama'*, an Ayurvedic term meaning a toxic by-product of poor digestion. It is this *'ama'* that is thought to lead to a great deal of the chronic health problems endemic in our Western diet (diabetes, obesity, arthritis, high blood pressure, immunity disorders, IBS, asthma and eczema).

In the West we tend to eat just two or three flavours in our daily diet, (processed food is mainly all salt and sugar), which then doesn't satiate all the other taste receptors on the tongue. Generally, we are not eating enough pungent, bitter and sour tastes, and tend to over-indulge on sweet and salty tastes and crave more of them.

In Ayurveda, each taste has a direct effect on our well-being. So, if we miss out on several tastes in a meal, and over-indulge the others, we create too much of some effects, which our body struggles to deal with. Our bodies want to receive equal measures of each taste, to provide adequate fuel for all the metabolic processes and responses inside us. It is, therefore, so important to provide a perfect balance of tastes, in every meal, for all sorts of health reasons: satiation; efficient fuel for our body's metabolism; fuelling our cells; repairing our organs, including our brain (especially as we get older and live for longer); giving us energy and avoiding toxic build ups.

When food is fully digested and easily absorbed into our body's tissues it helps our body re-generate, as well as efficiently removing worn-out structures and toxins. Our bodies become energised, strong and stable, and we feel happy and healthy. When food is perfectly balanced it affects both our mind and body.

I was taught that in Ayurveda all food should ideally be chopped up as small as possible before it is eaten. This serves a number of purposes. It gives your stomach less work to do when digesting. It makes it easier to taste the six tastes at the same time. It also increases the speed of food assimilation into our gut and reduces unnecessary extra strain on our gut.

This is important as 95% of the serotonin ('happiness hormone') we produce is manufactured in the cells of our gut. So by reducing stress on our gut, we are preserving more energy for it to go on making that lovely serotonin for us. You can see how food has a direct effect on our gut. 'Anyone suffering from anxiety or depression should remember that an unhappy gut can be the cause of an unhappy mind.'
(Guilia Enders, Gut: The Inside Story)

Most people in the West take their vitamins in capsule form, swallowing them without tasting them and thereby reducing their therapeutic value. The stomach has no taste buds, so when the majority of vitamins are eaten in this way, the effects and benefits derived from the taste are almost zero. Ayurveda emphasises the importance of us tasting all of our food, in order to fully enjoy its health benefits.

THE TASTES

SALTY — aids digestion, creates new building blocks. Solid and reliable people are called 'the salt of the earth.' Salt is a very strong flavour, so you don't need much of it to balance the tastes. It cleanses body tissues, balances the nervous system, and activates digestion. It is also a mild laxative and anti-spasmodic. We eat too much of it in the West.

Excess: causes ulcers, aggravates stomach acidity, water retention, thirst, oedema and high blood pressure.

Examples: all salts, all seafood, most fish, bacon, olives, celery

BITTER — detoxifies and balances the body, reduces stress. It tones the organs, cleanses the liver, and controls skin ailments, promotes bowel motions and urination. It excels in clearing itching and swelling of the skin. It also acts as an appetite stimulant to clear the palate and encourage the release of digestive enzymes. It scrapes away fatty deposits and so is useful for weight loss. It can balance emotion, calm anger and reduce stress. In high doses it can be used as a natural antibiotic.

The bitter flavour found in plants is often attributed to a defence mechanism – if you taste nasty, no one will eat you! Plants with bitter compounds are well known for their anti-inflammatory, anti-bacterial and digestive properties.

Excess: can weaken the kidneys, reduce reproductive tissue and can encourage fear and anxiety.

Examples: coffee, all greens, dark chocolate, chicory, turmeric, rhubarb, spinach

SOUR — good for the heart and warms the body. It cleanses your digestion. Another strong flavour so not needed in vast quantities to create balance. It helps eliminate waste from the body. It increases moisture in our mouth and increases the flow of saliva, which is vital for pushing food to our stomach, without creating flatulence.

Sour fruits are high in vitamin C and are considered to be anti-oxidants, rejuvenators and tonics.

Excess: causes dizziness, thirst, burning sensations, hyper-acidity, ulcers, fever, itching, anaemia, and skin diseases. It can also aggravate diarrhoea, oedema, wet coughs and congestive problems.

Examples: citrus fruit, yoghurt, vinegar

ASTRINGENT — heals the body and binds the body together by its restrictive nature. It reduces secretions such as bleeding, excessive sweating, urination, diarrhoea, and excess catarrh. By holding the tissues together it heals wounds, and prevents flaccid and loose tissue from accumulating.

Excess: can cause body stiffening, heart pain, convulsions, gas and urine retention, and constipation.

Examples: lentils, apples, pears, courgettes, asparagus, green beans, lettuce, walnuts

PUNGENT — stimulates our appetite and metabolism and balances secretions from the body. It helps lung problems by drying the excess mucus and moisture and relieves colds and bronchitis. It helps weight loss by stimulating our metabolism and reducing fat.

Excess: can reduce semen production, cause constipation, intestinal inflammation, bleeding, dizziness, urinary retention and excessive dryness.

Examples: some spices and herbs, onions, garlic

SWEET — provides grounding, increases and heals body tissues, nourishes and comforts the body and relieves hunger. It increases the integrity of the immune system. It benefits our minds, lungs, digestive, urinary and reproductive systems.

Excess: decreases digestive strength, thus increases weight gain, increases mucus and promotes congestion. It can cause fever, breathing problems, swollen lymph glands, flaccidity, heaviness, obesity, fungal infections and diabetes. It creates cravings for more of it.

Examples: carrots, honey, cucumber, almonds, sesame seeds, grains

Obviously there are many foods that have more than one taste, for example lemons are both sour and astringent. However, the secret is always to maintain a balance of all six tastes. So if I use lemon in my recipes for its sourness, I have added another food for astringency.

MY AYURVEDIC JOURNEY

One week in 2008, Ayurvedic cooking did for me what six weeks of strong antibiotics and three doctors had failed to achieve. Out of the blue on Christmas Eve, having spent the whole day lambing in the freezing wind and rain in north Hampshire on our small farm, I very suddenly came down with pneumonia. It was a complete shock. I have always been a very healthy outdoorsy sort of person. I didn't actually believe I had it. It was a particularly serious bout which dragged an emergency doctor from his Christmas lunch to my bed to administer enormous, seemingly horse-sized antibiotics, which I was instructed to take for the next two weeks.

Two weeks passed with no change in my health, which meant more antibiotics, and further changes of types antibiotics after that for another five to six weeks. The longer I spent confined to my bed, the more depressed and fed up I became. So I decided on impulse to find some sun and literally burn off the remains of the pneumonia I felt was still lurking inside my lung. It seemed that the only hot holiday I could go on alone, at the end of January, as a solo travelling woman feeling a bit vulnerable, was some sort of retreat, where I wouldn't need to talk to anyone.

So after a great deal of research, I booked a last-minute flight to Mauritius where the world famous (to Indians and possibly the rest of the Ayurvedic world, but not me!) Shanti Ananda Spa Retreat in the Himalayas, had just opened up its first sister retreat. I had no idea what I was letting myself in for, but thought it was worth a go, and it promised a full return to health and total rejuvenation within a week. I was pretty sceptical.

On arrival I discovered it was a full-on 'Ayurvedic immersion' retreat, starting with Dr Mani, a Himalayan Ayurvedic doctor assessing my dosha type, and then prescribing my personal Ayurvedic treatment for the rest of the week. He then crucially, I now believe, prescribed my menu for the entire week. The chef was given specific orders that I was only to be served that menu. No other options were available. There were only Ayurvedic 'treats' available in my room mini-bar (nuts, fruit and herbal teas). No sweet or dairy products, and no alcohol or caffeine in the form of either black tea or coffee.

On my first day I was still sneezing, shivering and generally unwell, but Dr Mani asked me to trust him and stop taking my antibiotics. He took them away from me and advised me to follow his Ayurvedic route back to health. I was terrified, as I had been completely dependent on my antibiotics for over six weeks. Still delirious with fever by then and having sweated and sneezed with a temperature of over 103 for the whole journey out there, I honestly didn't care. I handed him over all my antibiotics.

Dr Mani monitored me daily, taking my blood pressure, feeling pressure points in my wrist, and looking at my tongue. I was also continually checked up on, by the Ayurvedic chef and staff, who all seemed to know about me, so there was no getting out of my prescribed eating plan. They came to check up on me during my meals and while I was resting on the beach. They also made sure I went to the retreat's meditation sessions and ate at the right time. I was never lonely and made some great friends.

Five days later, I was not only completely well again and feeling healthier than I had for years but also actually incredibly calm inside, and strong in spirit. I felt I was ready to govern any country that would have me on my return. Which is from someone who isn't even that interested in politics, believe me!

My husband and daughters didn't recognise the new 'changed me' when they met me at the airport and thought I was on some sort of 'wacky backy' or something, as I felt so refreshed, well, strong and calm.

I realised that all it took was five days of Ayurvedic cooking to totally re-balance me back to health.

All the ingredients used by the Ayurvedic chef were fresh, mainly vegetarian and easy to find on any supermarket shelf. They were just prepared and cooked in a completely new way to me, and I must add, absolutely delicious. I also lost almost seven pounds in weight in five days, which was another surprise benefit.

It was a significant life-changer for me and it shocked me how quickly my body changed from being so sick to becoming so healthy in a matter of days, without any medicine at all. It also scared me slightly, to wake up to the fact that my dependence on the curative effects of clinical medicines can sometimes mask the fact that there are much simpler, cheaper, natural and possibly more powerful ways to achieve an overall better result.

Whilst out there I was so fascinated by this new technique of cooking for health that I pestered the chef for a couple of Ayurvedic cooking lessons while I was recovering. I also asked Dr Mani for more knowledge about Ayurveda and to explain its history and benefits, specifically in relation to food.

We discussed the idea of me writing a simple cookbook for Westerners who may have never come across Ayurvedic cooking. I wanted to make the recipes very quick and easy so they were as accessible as possible to everyone. I was totally hooked.

There were many principles I learnt from both Dr Mani and his chef, but the crucially different concept to any other form of cooking I had ever come across previously, was the Ayurvedic principle that you need to satiate all the six tastes on your tongue, in every meal and, if possible, within every mouthful, for rapid inner health. This was something totally new and exciting to me. So I decided to base my cookbook solely on this principle, and all my recipes contain ingredients that encompass all the six different tastes in every single dish.

I should point out that in Ayurveda it is believed there are six tastes you can pick up on your tongue, even though in the West we generally refer to just five. I will always be referring to the six Ayurvedic tastes in this book.

Dr Mani agreed to check all my recipes to ensure they were truly Ayurvedic and they followed as many of the strict Ayurvedic cooking principles as possible.

I have since been back to meet Dr Mani again, armed with all my recipes, and he very kindly went through them, giving extra advice where it was needed and filling in any gaps in my growing knowledge about Ayurveda.

Enjoy your Ayurvedic food journey!

WHAT IS AYURVEDA?

Understanding all of Ayurveda is complicated so I have broken its concepts down as simply as possible, and concentrated solely on the eating for health side of it. Hopefully this will make my book more accessible to those who may have never heard of it before.

Pronounced: 'eye-your-vay-dah' Ayurveda is a Sanskrit word meaning: 'knowledge of life' *ayus* – life *veda* – knowledge/science. Ayurveda comes from ancient India, and is over 5,000 years old. It is thought to have originated in the Himalayas and to be the oldest medicine known to mankind.

Ancient shamans existed in most villages and became experts in their local plants. They had the job of both being doctor and priest in their village. Each year they would travel up into the Himalayas for a month or so for a retreat to practice meditation, yoga and prayer. In particular, they discussed what herbal remedies had worked for them in their village over the past year. They would share this knowledge with the most senior shamans. The remedies were tried out again and again during the year, and any remedies that they believed worked particularly well would be incorporated into their Ayurveda practices.

This knowledge was then shared in subsequent years with all the village shamans to take away and use in their villages.

They explored the effects of taste, energy and specific actions of plants and minerals. It seems evident that these early holy men used their knowledge of herbs and diet for medicinal purposes to bestow overall health and wellbeing to the people of their villages.

Historically, the knowledge of Ayurveda was transmitted through Vedas, ancient songs. The oldest song known is the 'Rig Veda' ('in praise of knowledge') that is almost 5,000 years old, and describes healing herbs and how they can be used.

Unfortunately, when the Moghul invaders and the British Raj took over India, they banned all Ayurvedic medicine or health techniques, branding them as nonsense. Therefore, a great deal of the ancient Ayurveda knowledge was lost, and remained known only to Himalayan families who had passed it down for generations, or to villages which were not governed by the British, namely most of southern India. This is why anyone who has visited southern India, for example Kerala, may have come across some form of Ayurveda.

In 1970 the Central Council for Ayurveda was created. This was to oversee the standards and practices of Ayurveda companies selling ready-prepared Ayurvedic remedies, using mixes of various spices and herbs. The 19th and 20th centuries saw a revival in Ayurveda with the building of new Ayurveda colleges. Approximately 100 were built in India in 1983.

Ayurveda is often used today as a generic term for traditional Indian medicine. However, it is about more than just medicine. It is about a whole healthy lifestyle, of which food is one of the most important factors. Ayurveda believes that disease is often due to a dysfunction in the inner processes of the body or mind as a whole. This is different to our modern view of disease, which examines organs in isolation. We need to think of our body as an eco-system and provide it with the correct food and balance of food to support it.

'Ayurveda tells us which substances, qualities and actions are life enhancing and which are not' (Charaka Samhita, written circa 150 BC).

Ayurveda teaches an understanding of your 'dosha-type' and to avoid things that increase your dosha. Dosha means 'fault' i.e. your imbalances. Ayurveda is all about creating balance, and this can be done very powerfully through Ayurvedic cooking.

When your dosha type is unbalanced, it leads to all sort of problems, physically, mentally and spiritually. It is therefore important to re-balance it. According to Ayurveda un-balanced doshas are the cause of most chronic diseases.

'Dosha' is the Ayurvedic term that describes our inherited traits, individual characteristics and tendencies. This refers to body frame, eye colour, digestive capability, emotional balance, as well as disease tendencies.

There are three dosha types:

Vata comprised of space and wind – vata people are fast moving, pro-active and communicative

Pitta made up of fire and water – pitta people are passionate, energetic and eager

Kapha combination of earth and water – kapha people are steady, and emotionally and physically strong

(See appendix at the end of my book, for full details of the three dosha types, together with questionnaires to see which dosha type you are likely to be.)

HEALTH BENEFITS

'Let food be your medicine and medicine your food.'
Hippocrates

Ayurvedic health was based on food being your medicine as there was no other medicine around 5,000 years ago. The idea was that healthy food gave you a healthy gut, and a healthy gut gave you a healthy body and mind.

Recently, Professor Tim Spector, of Kings College London, has produced compelling scientific evidence that gut health has possibly the most significant effect on our complete health. He believes that the bacteria in our gut hold amazing powers over our health and mood. His belief is supported by a great deal of contemporary scientific research which underlines the power of the gut and the human micro-flora (good and bad bacteria) that live within it. The bacteria are nourished or destroyed by what we eat. Ayurveda was saying the same thing over 5,000 years ago, by emphasising the importance of the digestive system for overall health.

Eating is the most important activity that can affect your health. What we choose to consume, is one of the only things we can control that affects our internal organs. The Japanese are much more interested in their gut health than the British and have a strong desire to eat healthy food. They consume very few vitamins in the form of pills/capsules, they receive all their vitamins from their food. It seems no coincidence then that they also top the global life expectancy league.

Degenerative and chronic conditions are becoming more commonplace today and we have lost a lot of our understanding about our well-being and what our body needs. We are more obsessed by health and diet than ever and yet we are experiencing an epidemic of obesity and allergies, which demonstrates our lack of understanding of what a healthy diet actually is. My belief is that we need to eat a far more varied and balanced diet. Cutting edge research has shown that the more diverse our diet, the better it is for us. Our ancestors' diet was 20 times more varied than ours. Now our modern diet comes from just five foods — corn, wheat, meat, sugar and soy — which are all found in processed foods. We should give our bodies the best head start that we can. Ayurvedically balanced food will allow our bodies to function more efficiently. This should help us to minimise future health problems, and help us to live younger longer.

Known Ayurvedic food benefits:

- Loss of excess weight
- Increased energy and health
- Increased wellbeing
- Increased immunity
- Increased strength physically, emotionally and spiritually
- Increased protection against chronic diseases
- Increased rejuvenation
- Reduced stress

AYURVEDIC FOOD

Ayurvedic food is all about balance and in order to be completely satisfied and satiated after each meal we need to balance the six tastes. In the West we depend on processed foods for speed and convenience and tend to eat too much of only two of the six tastes, namely sugar and salt. They are present in so many of our meals and snacks, either hidden (for example in breakfast cereals, low-fat yoghurts, ready-made meals) or not (for example, salted crisps, chips, hamburgers) and because of this we are never satiated after eating.

The six tastes, when eaten together, satisfy all our taste receptors. This in turn satisfies all our stomach enzymes and creates the feeling of flavour-balance and satiation. This happens after eating the equivalent of only two or three tablespoons of Ayurvedically balanced food. So you are actually eating less too.

When eating Ayurvedic food, the feeling of satiation lasts much longer than after eating our usual Western meals. Ayurvedic food also makes you feel much healthier, more energetic and stronger for longer. It has the added benefit of creating a sense of well-being so you feel calmer and sleep better. This is because you are balancing your nutrition perfectly to your body's needs. In the West our diet is often completely at odds with what our body needs to function correctly. This has led to the common health problems we encounter now which are well documented both in the press and within scientific reports.

Ayurveda places great emphasis on digestion and metabolism. Every year we replace 98% of our atoms, the building blocks of our bodies. This means that every year, nearly all our body tissues are replaced and our body is continually changing. This is good news for us. It means we can control what we eat and make ourselves healthy again at any time. Our digestive tract (gut) is the most active organ in our body and it can be changed by diet very quickly.

This book is designed so that you can dip and dive into the recipes, whenever you feel you need a quick health boost. Or you can use the recipes over a longer period of time for more powerful health benefits. If you are not feeling healthy or energised, you can help yourself, simply by taking care of your digestion, by re-balancing your meals Ayurvedically. In doing so you will stimulate your metabolism, which will give you more energy. This will start strengthening your tissues and help your body cleanse itself of toxins.

Ayurvedic balance affects the mind and spirit as well as the body.
A famous Ayurvedic saying is:

'sarvepi roga mandagni'   which translates to

'all disease is caused by extreme emotions or an inappropriate diet'

As I don't have a background as a chef or an Ayurvedic practitioner, my approach to these recipes has been to create meals that are simple as well as quick and easy to make at home. My background as a botanist has heavily influenced me. I worked for Marks and Spencer as a vegetable specialist for twelve years, and therefore my recipes are also drawn on scientific knowledge and have been reinforced by my understanding of food technology and a personal belief that plants offer us some of the most powerful medicines and health benefits possible. Plant based food is a form of natural medicine. Plants are a very cheap way of getting our natural medicine as well as our nutrition.

Whilst working for Marks and Spencer, I travelled extensively around the world and learnt where the best vegetables grew, what gave them the best flavour and what their nutritional values were. However, I knew nothing at all about Eastern nutrition.

To further my research, in 2012, I was invited to attend the UK's first 'International Functional Food' conference in Oxford. A 'Functional Food' is defined as something that does more than just nourish you, it provides additional scientifically-proven health benefits.

Functional foods have been coined 'superfoods' by the media. Plant sterols, are a proven functional food, which lower cholesterol and naturally occur in grains, vegetables, fruits, nuts and seeds. Following the conference I came to realise that the plants used in Ayurvedic medicine and food were often the same as those being researched by the scientists from all over the world as functional foods. Functional food science is a relatively new area of scientific research. The term functional food was only established 10-15 years ago. However, it seems that Ayurveda has appreciated the benefits of these 'superfoods' for thousands of years.

Another rather depressing fact from the conference was that the UK is the most food-science phobic nation in the world!

Anyway, enough of the science, I have added my notes from the conference to the back of this book for anyone wanting to read more.

First and foremost, my book is a completely new approach to cooking which I hope will change the way you think and prepare your meals and make you and your family much happier and healthier. All the recipes are delicious, simple to make and more importantly take less than 30 minutes to prepare and cook. The cooking is mainly done in just one pan. So incredibly simple!

All the recipes are my own creations and so I apologise if I have got some of the quantities of the ingredients slightly wrong. It has been a labour of love to get all these recipes into a book after years of testing them on my family and friends and then asking Dr Mani, my Ayurvedic doctor, to also check them. The main thing to remember is that as long as you use all the six tastes in each meal it doesn't matter so much the quantities, just ensure that all the tastes are balanced.

All the ingredients are natural and widely available in supermarkets.

MY AYURVEDIC COOKING PRINCIPLES

Food is one of the few aspects of our health that we can control, so it makes sense to eat healthily and understand what we eat and why. Traditional Ayurveda explains in great detail how and when to eat for each dosha type. For example, I am mainly Vata and so should eat my first meal at 6am and it should consist of nuts and fruits, and eat my last meal at 6pm.

As this is impossible for me with my lifestyle — as I am never up at 6am and don't ever finish work until after 6pm — I have tempered the main Ayurveda rules with the constraints of my modern lifestyle.

Ayurvedic cooking is fairly heavily vegetarian, but occasionally adds some seafood, white meat or fish to its dishes. This is due to the fact that red meat is difficult and slow to digest and so goes against the Ayurvedic principle of maintaining an efficient digestive system. It is also thought that too much red meat is not particularly good for our overall health, causing build up in 'ama' (toxins) within our bodies, that can take days to get rid of. Most food, on average, takes only a day from fork to excretion. Faster guts and faster digesting foods can accomplish it in less than four hours. This leaves the gut time to 'clean up' after digestion. Scientists nickname this cleaning process the little 'housekeeper'. Constant snacking, or continually eating foods with long digestion times, means there is no time for cleaning. By eating our food in small bite-sized pieces, we give our housekeeper more time to get on with her essential work. However, for all you meat lovers, my Ayurvedic doctor assured me that eating red meat once or twice a week would be fine. Due to the nature of Ayurvedic cooking, much of it is done very quickly on the hob, so that the energy of the food (and vitamins and nutrients) is retained and it's plant enzymes are not denatured by over-cooking.

Sanskrit teachings (the ancient Ayurvedic language), state that the volume of food that can be held in your two cupped hands, is designed by nature to fill your stomach. Just one handful for a child. Therefore, my recipes are based on these size portions. It may surprise you that your whole family will feel this is plenty. They should feel fuller, more satiated and more energetic, after eating the equivalent of two handfuls of an Ayurvedic meal, than they would have eating the larger amounts we commonly eat in the West.

These are the Ayurvedic food principles I learnt that struck me as particularly useful and easy to use in our everyday cooking:

- **Always combine the six tastes in each meal. I have colour-coded the tastes in every list of ingredients, so you can see where you are getting each taste in every meal.**

- As Ayurveda is based on digestion, ideally all food should be cut up into small pieces, especially meat, for more rapid digestion and less build up of toxins.

41

This also enables you to taste all the six tastes in one mouthful. As different foods require different digestive enzymes, certain foods do not combine particularly well together in the stomach. I have avoided these combinations wherever possible in my recipes.

Ayurveda suggests that we digest foods in a specific taste order: sweet, salty, sour, pungent, bitter and astringent. So if we finish a meal with a sweet pudding, our digestive system gets confused and starts all over again. It thinks there is another meal on its way. So although a small amount of sweetness at the end of a meal is fine, a small sweet snack later on in the afternoon would be better. The French habit of eating cheese at the end of their meals is more in tune with Ayurvedic principles.

It is better to avoid too much red meat because it can be difficult for us to digest, especially late at night. You will know the feeling only too well of undigested red meat, sitting in your stomach all night long, after a late meal. It can take over 72 hours to digest red meat.

If you can, avoid eating anything late at night. When we are asleep we are in semi-hibernation: 50-60% of our food is still undigested which is also why our breath may smell of undigested food the next morning! At night we only digest at 55% of our midday rate, which is why it is better to eat your main meal at lunchtime or even breakfast.

○ Try to add turmeric to almost every meal you can because it is thought to be an Ayurvedic 'wonder spice' (also scientifically proven as a 'superfood' – see appendix). Turmeric easily provides your bitterness quota, needed in each meal, without you really tasting it. In the Himalayas it is used to:

- soften skin
- as an antiseptic
- as an anti-inflammatory
- as a hot poultice to reduce swelling and bruising (mix in hot water and add to bandage)
- as an anti-carcinogen

○ Soups are an excellent form of Ayurvedic food as they are quickly digested and absorbed.

○ It's a great idea to introduce seeds, grains and nuts to meals to increase digestive mobility.

○ Black pepper should always be added to food as it improves the uptake of nutrients in the body.

○ Always add a squeeze of lemon juice — a great cleanser. Both lemon and honey help break things down fast in your body and have wonderfully therapeutic qualities.

∾ Where possible try to use rock salt to replace your usual table salt as it is packed full of beneficial minerals.

∾ Always add herbs and spices as they create the balance of tastes in a lot of meals and are exceptionally therapeutic. Herbs and spices also provide natural antiseptic and anti-inflammatory benefits from their essential oils. They are our natural food medicine cabinet.

I wish you well on your adventures with Ayurvedic cooking. It has changed my life and it can change yours.

RECIPES

All my recipes have been designed to incorporate the six tastes, in every mouthful, so that you feel the immediate satiation effect of having all six tastes satisfied. They use modern Western ingredients that you will easily find in most large supermarkets and independent food shops.

As this is an Ayurvedic cookbook I wanted to try and create recipes for all three of the 'dosha' types (see appendix for more details), yet try and keep things simple by making each recipe as tri-doshic as possible (suits all three dosha types).

However, when I have used food that isn't so good for a particular dosha type, I have used a food 'antidote' to offset its effect. For example to antidote the effect of potatoes on Vata people, I have added black pepper and cumin.

You will notice that I have included quite a few soups. This is intentional, because soup is the quickest way to digest and absorb all the six tastes into our bodies and reduce the chances of blockages and build-up of toxins.

Cooking with herbs and spices brings flavour and aroma to your food. It also helps the food to become more digestible and balance the six tastes. The most useful spices are fresh ginger, cumin, coriander, fennel seed, cardamom, oregano, mint, paprika, yellow mustard seeds and turmeric. I usually run a mile when I see a recipe with over 15 ingredients, but the spices are what 'make the difference' and are generally what we lack in most of our Western cooking today. They really are essential for the whole Ayurvedic concept of health and balance.

My Ayurvedic chef taught me to sometimes add a splash of water to the oil at the start of cooking and sometimes during cooking. This was so that the ingredients never cook too fiercely, but just slightly soften and always remain moist. It also blends their tastes into each other better. Most significantly, it aids the overall balance of the six tastes. At any stage during the cooking process, feel free to add another splash or two of water, to loosen up the ingredients and mix their tastes/flavours/aromas.

The trick with my recipes is to have all the ingredients prepared, before you start any of the dishes. Most the ingredients will need chopping up into diced sized pieces before cooking. Then all the recipes can be cooked in about 20-30 minutes. Each recipe is enough for approximately four people.

Main spices and herbs to keep in your cupboard:

- Yellow mustard seeds
- Cayenne pepper
- Paprika
- Fenugreek
- Turmeric
- Coriander seeds
- Cumin seeds
- Caraway seeds
- Cardamom pods
- Fennel seeds
- Tarragon
- Oregano
- Chilli flakes
- Thyme
- Ginger
- Rock salt
- Black pepper

TURMERIC PRIMER

Drinking a small amount of warm water, ideally with turmeric and specific digestive spices, before each meal, is an Ayurvedic pre-meal practice, to prime the digestive system. Therefore I recommend the following short drink before each of your main meals.

One shot glass of:

- Warm water
- Sprinkle of turmeric
- Sprinkle of ground ginger
- Squeeze lime/lemon
- Sprinkle of celery salt
- Sprinkle of freshly ground black pepper
- Sprinkle of cumin seeds

SOUPS

Soups are an excellent way of eating Ayurvedically,
balancing all six tastes, with many different nutritious vegetables, in
a quickly and easily digestible form.

MUSHROOM & ASPARAGUS SOUP

*For additional flavour use brown or Portobello mushrooms - a delicious recipe
to cook during the English asparagus season in early summer.*

serves 4

1 tbsp grated parmesan	1 tsp yellow mustard seeds
1 lime juice	1 tsp paprika
½ lemon juice	splash Tabsaco sauce
2 cups diced asparagus	1 tsp cumin seeds
2 diced garlic cloves	½ tsp coriander seeds
splash olive oil	1½ pints vegetable stock
2 cups diced mushrooms	black pepper
½ tsp turmeric	rock salt

Gently fry the mustard, cumin and coriander seeds in olive oil, for a minute, to bring out the
aromatics. Then add garlic, mushrooms and asparagus until softened. Add turmeric, Tabasco
and paprika and cook for a further five minutes. When all ingredients are softened and
fragrant, pour in vegetable stock. Allow to simmer for 15 minutes. Add half the parmesan
and lime and lemon juice. Season to taste. Blitz in a food processor, or with
a hand blender until smooth. Finally garnish
with remaining parmesan.

SEARED SALMON & CAULIFLOWER SOUP

A handsome looking dish with flakes of freshly seared warm salmon,
scattered over a zingy, nutty cauliflower soup.

serves 4

1 slice of fresh salmon	1 tsp paprika
1 fresh lime juice	1 tsp cumin seeds
1 cupful white wine	1 tbsp pumpkin seeds
2 cups chopped green beans	1 tsp yellow mustard seeds
1 tbsp chopped fresh ginger	1 tsp turmeric
1tbsp sesame seeds	1 pint vegetable stock
1 cauliflower in florets	2 tbsp olive oil
1 diced large onion	black pepper

Gently toast mustard and cumin seeds in oil. Add chopped onion and fry until translucent. Sprinkle with paprika and turmeric. Add sesame and pumpkin seeds, and cook for a couple of minutes, stirring until fragrant ensuring everything is coated well with the spices. Add cauliflower florets, green beans, veg stock, lime and white wine. Bring to the boil and simmer for 15-20 minutes, until vegetables are soft. Blitz in a food processor until smooth. Meanwhile, sear salmon on both sides, on a hot griddle or pan. Serve soup garnished with flakes of the seared salmon and black pepper.

CHICKEN & SWEETCORN SOUP

An immune boosting and warming soup. I was served
this for three days during my illness.

serves 4

1 tbsp grated parmesan	1 diced onion
1 tsp fenugreek	1 tsp yellow mustard seeds
1 lemon juice	1 tsp fennel seeds
1 tbsp pine nuts	1 tsp turmeric
2 tbsp chopped fresh ginger	1 tbsp black pepper
1 tin of sweetcorn	1 juice of fresh lime
2 cooked diced chicken breasts	1 pint veg stock
1 cup diced mushrooms	splash of sesame oil
2 cloves of diced garlic	rock salt

Heat sesame oil in a pan. Add mustard, pine nuts, fennel and fenugreek and stir gently to release their aromatics. Then add garlic, onion and ginger and stir gently until soft. Add mushrooms and turmeric, keep stirring and cook for five minutes. Add chicken, stir/cook for a further five minutes until slightly brown. Add lemon and lime juice, sweetcorn, seasoning and veg stock. Bring to boil and simmer for 15-20 minutes. Whizz soup to smooth consistency in a blender. Stir in parmesan and serve.

CELERY & APPLE SOUP

The fresh apple balances the salty celery, and the chilli flakes
give this soup an unexpected kick.

serves 4

4 sticks chopped celery	pinch chilli flakes
½ chopped fresh chicory	½ tsp coriander seeds
2 tbsp yoghurt	1 tsp tarragon
1 diced green apple	½ tsp turmeric
1 diced onion	1 tsp cumin seeds
1 cup diced cucumber	1 pint veg stock
1 cup diced potato	½ lemon juice
3 diced cloves garlic	3 tbsp olive oil
1 tsp yellow mustard seeds	black pepper
1 tsp dried or fresh thyme	rock salt

Gently fry mustard, coriander and cumin seeds until fragrant in olive oil. Then add onion and garlic and cook until soft. Sprinkle with turmeric and coat the onion and garlic with all the spices. Cook for a further minute stirring all the time. Add the potato, apple, (I leave the apple skin on as it is full of vitamins and it gets mushed up in the soup, but it is up to you) celery, chicory and veg stock and bring to the boil. Add thyme, cucumber, chilli flakes, tarragon and lemon juice. Turn heat down and simmer for approximately 15-20 minutes, until everything is soft and cooked through. Blitz until smooth, and add yoghurt to thicken. Serve hot or cold with seasoning to taste.

CAULIFLOWER SOUP

A lightly spiced, fresh flavoured soup. Cauliflower is used widely in Ayurvedic cooking.
It is also one of my favourite vegetables.

serves 4

1 tbsp Tabasco	½ tsp cumin seeds
½ tsp fenugreek	1 tsp turmeric
1 glass white wine	1 handful fresh chopped rosemary
1 small diced cauliflower	4 small sprigs fresh chopped thyme
2 cloves diced garlic	1 pint veg stock
1 tbsp milk	black pepper
3-4 diced new potatoes	½ lemon juice
1 tsp yellow mustard seeds	1 tbsp olive oil

Dry fry the cumin and mustard seeds together, then add garlic with a little oil until soft.
Add the cauliflower, potatoes, fenugreek and turmeric and a splash of water, if necessary to
mix well, and stir until well combined. Add the veg stock, wine, milk, rosemary and thyme, and
bring to boil. Simmer together for 15-20 minutes until soft and well cooked.
Add Tabasco, lemon juice and black pepper to taste.
Whizz soup in a blender and serve hot.

CARROT & CORIANDER SOUP

A classic pairing of sweet carrots with punchy, fresh coriander which gets the Ayurvedic treatment in this delicious, lightly spiced soup.

serves 4

2 tsp Tabasco	1 tbsp diced ginger
1 lime juice and zest	½ tsp caraway seeds
2 tbsp orange juice & zest	½ tsp cumin seeds
2 diced asparagus spears	2 tsp dried oregano
1 large diced onion	½ tsp cayenne pepper
4 large diced carrots	1 pint veg stock
bunch fresh chopped coriander	½ tsp turmeric
1 diced sweet potato	rock salt
4 cloves chopped garlic	black pepper
2 tsp coriander seeds	2 tbsp olive oil

Toast caraway, cumin and coriander seeds in a splash of oil, and add onions and cook for five minutes. Add garlic, ginger, oregano, cayenne pepper, and turmeric, cook for one minute. Add carrots, asparagus and sweet potato, stir well. Coat all surfaces with spices, add splash of water to help mix, and cook for 10 minutes, stirring all the time. Add veg stock, orange and lime juice, zest, and Tabasco, and simmer for 20 minutes until soft. Add fresh coriander, whizz to blend into a soup, and serve with a sprig of fresh coriander on top. Add seasoning to taste.

LENTIL & SMOKED LARDON SOUP

A firm, hearty, family favourite, all year round soup. I just love this flavour combination.
You can substitute lemon for lime.

serves 4

1 handful smoked bacon lardons	1 tsp cumin seeds
½ **diced chicory**	1 tsp yellow mustard seeds
3 tbsp yoghurt	1 tsp turmeric
1 tin cooked lentils	2 bay leaves
1 small diced onion	1 tbsp chopped thyme
1 small diced carrot	1 lime juice
½ stick diced celery	1 pint veg stock
2 cloves chopped garlic	2 tbsp olive oil
1 tbsp pre-soaked almonds	rock salt
1 tsp coriander seeds	black pepper

Fry the mustard, cumin and coriander seeds on medium heat. Add lardons until lightly browned. In the same pan add the onion, carrot, almonds, celery, chicory, and garlic (scraping up all the sticky bits from the bottom of the pan) for a few minutes until soft and the onions are translucent. Add the turmeric and stir for one minute with the lime juice. Add lentils and season to taste. Add veg stock, bay leaves and thyme. Simmer for 20 minutes and whizz using blender. Stir in yoghurt and serve.

GINGER & LIME SOUP

For my Asian inspired soup it is important to use both fresh ginger and fresh lime to bring out its full tangy flavour.

serves 4

1 diced celery stalk	3 sprigs chopped fresh coriander
3 limes, juice & zest	1 tin coconut milk
1 lemon juice	1 tsp turmeric
2 diced asparagus	splash of soy sauce
1 tbsp chopped ginger	1 tsp yellow mustard seeds
3 diced carrots	1 tsp cumin seeds
1 large chopped onion	1 zest of fresh orange
2 cloves chopped garlic	2 tbsp olive oil
1 small chopped green chilli	seasoning

Fry mustard and cumin seeds in oil and then add garlic, ginger, onion and turmeric until fragrant and softened. Add the asparagus, celery, chilli, soy sauce and carrots. Stir fry to combine well. Then add coconut milk and simmer for 15-20 minutes until everything is cooked and tender. Add coriander (reserving some to garnish), juice of lemon and limes, and lime and orange zest. Season well with coarsely ground black pepper and rock salt to taste. Whizz in a blender. Serve with fresh coriander on top.

MACKEREL, BEAN & HORSERADISH SOUP

Mackerel is a favourite of mine. It is an oily fish, packed with Omega-3, and high levels of protein, providing a wide range of health benefits. Its combination with horseradish sauce is a match made in heaven.

serves 4

1 large smoked mackerel, flaked	1 tsp yellow mustard seeds
1 tsp turmeric	½ tsp coriander seeds
1 lemon juice & zest	1 tbsp fresh basil
2 cups frozen broad beans	1 tbsp fresh mint
5 diced spring onions	1 tbsp fresh rosemary
2 tbsp olive oil	1 pint veg stock
1 tbsp horseradish sauce	1 tbsp Tabasco
2 cloves garlic	black pepper

Fry the mustard and coriander seeds in a splash of oil for a few seconds then add the garlic. Meanwhile par-boil the beans for one minute in boiling water. Add the beans and spring onions to the spice mix and stir for two-three minutes. Add the mackerel, fresh herbs, and turmeric, and stir for a minute. Add the veg stock and Tabasco. Simmer for 15-20 minutes. Finally add the horseradish sauce, lemon juice and zest. Whizz in a blender. Serve with black pepper on top.

WOOD SORREL & NETTLE SOUP

Created after spotting both nettles and wood sorrel growing together in the woods on a recent walk with my youngest daughter. If you can't find the often elusive wild wood sorrel, use a green apple instead.

serves 4

1 carrier bag fresh nettle leaves	handful of fresh coriander
1 tsp turmeric	handful of fresh mint
3 tbsp yoghurt	2 tsp sesame seeds
1 cup chopped wood sorrel	2 tsp dried tarragon
1 diced onion	1 tbsp pumpkin seeds
½ cucumber diced	1 lemon
2 diced potatoes	1½ pint veg stock
½ tsp coriander seeds	black pepper
½ tsp cumin seeds	rock salt
1 tsp yellow mustard seeds	2 tbsp olive oil

Fry mustard, coriander and cumin seeds for a minute in the oil to release aromatics. Add onion and cook until soft and translucent. Add potatoes and stir continuously with a splash of water to loosen and mix spices. Sprinkle with turmeric and cook for a further minute. Add the vegetable stock, nettles, cucumber, sorrel/apple, fresh coriander, pumpkin seeds, mint, tarragon, lemon juice and zest. Simmer for 20 minutes, then whizz in blender until smooth. Add yoghurt and seasoning to taste.

COURGETTE & WATERCRESS SOUP

A great way to use up all your surplus home-grown
courgettes in the summer months.

serves 4

2 tbsp parmesan	2 tbsp yoghurt
½ tsp turmeric	black pepper
1 lemon juice & zest	1 tbsp sesame oil
3 diced medium courgettes	1 tsp yellow mustard seeds
1 bag chopped watercress	½ tsp cumin seeds
2 tsp sesame seeds	1 pint veg stock

Fry the mustard, sesame and cumin seeds in the oil for a minute to bring out the aromatics.
Add the courgettes and cook on medium heat until soft. Add the turmeric and bind into the
courgettes. Add the veg stock and watercress and simmer for 15 minutes. Add the yoghurt and
parmesan and keep stirring. Stir in the black pepper, lemon juice and zest. Serve with
a swirl of yoghurt in the middle of the soup.

STARTERS / SNACKS

For when you just feel like having a healthy snack
or a quick and easy starter.

AVOCADO & BEAN HUMMUS

Hummus is an excellent alternative to soup as a starter. It is also a great snack for whenever you are feeling hungry or just want a light lunch. It is quickly digested by the body, so is very good for you. Delicious with rye bread, pitta, chapatis or tortillas.

Takes only 5 minutes, and freezes really well - so make lots!

serves 4-6

1 tsp Tabasco	½ tsp rock salt
½ lime juice	¼ tsp black pepper
2 tbsp sour cream	2 tbsp mayonnaise
1 tbsp pine nuts	2 tbsp mozzarella cheese
1 bunch spring onions chopped	1 tsp turmeric
2 medium avocados	1 tsp mustard seeds
1 tin cannellini beans	½ tsp cumin seeds
1 tbsp lemon juice	½ tsp coriander seeds

Dry roast the mustard, coriander and cumin seeds. Put all the rest of the ingredients and the cooked spices into a blender.

Serve or freeze.

BEETROOT & WALNUT HUMMUS

I love this hummus for its amazing flavour and colour.
Freezes well.

serves 4-6

1 tsp Tabasco	½ tsp yellow mustard seeds
2 tbsp pre-soaked walnuts	½ tsp coriander seeds
1 lemon juice & zest	1 large garlic clove
1 tin cooked chickpeas	1 tbsp tahini (sesame seed paste)
6 diced radishes	1 diced cooking apple/2 dessert apples
1 jar pre-cooked beetroot cubes	1 tsp turmeric
½ tsp cumin seeds	1 tbsp sesame oil

Heat the oil and add mustard, cumin and coriander seeds. Gently fry them, shaking constantly to release aroma for one minute. In a blender mix walnuts, chickpeas and beetroot to a fine paste. Add all other ingredients and blend.
Add oil to loosen if required.

SPINACH HUMMUS

A wonderful fresh green hummus.

Freezes well.

serves 4-6

½ diced celery stalk	½ green chilli finely chopped
2 cups fresh spinach	1 bunch fresh parsley chopped
2 tbsp lemon juice	1 lime juice
1 can cooked chickpeas	1 tbsp sour cream
2 cloves garlic diced	1 tbsp mayonnaise
½ **diced cucumber**	rock salt
2 diced spring onions	black pepper

In a blender pulse garlic, spring onions and chilli until blended. Pulse parsley for few seconds only. Add spinach and pulse again. Add all remaining ingredients and blend until just mixed.

GRILLED OLIVES

Quick and easy, this is a healthy
crowd pleasing nibble.

serves 4

1 cup grated parmesan	1 lime juice and zest
1 jar olives stuffed with almonds	1 tsp smoked paprika
1 lemon juice	1 tsp turmeric
2 tsp poppy/chia seeds	1 pinch rock salt
1 tbsp Dijon mustard	black pepper
1 tsp honey	3 bay leaves

Mix the honey, poppy seeds and turmeric together. Place the olives onto a baking tray.
Coat with the honey mix. Add seasoning, and lemon and lime juice and zest. Sprinkle
with grated parmesan. Grill under low heat for 5-10 minutes.
Finally sprinkle with a little paprika to serve.

COURGETTE BAKE

This recipe is perfect for a summer al fresco starter, when courgettes are in season and at their freshest. It has a special place in my heart, as it was the first Ayurvedic recipe I created years ago, and is still loved by everyone I cook it for. It is beautiful in both looks and taste, and incredibly quick and simple to make.

serves 4

2 tbsp freshly grated parmesan	15-20 capers
1 tsp turmeric	12-15 sliced cherry tomatoes
3 tbsp mayonnaise	1 lime juice
3 sliced courgettes (5mm slices)	1 fresh lemon juice and zest
3 finely chopped spring onions	1 tbsp water
3 tbsp dry breadcrumbs	seasoning

Beat mayonnaise with water. Mix breadcrumbs, turmeric, salt, pepper, spring onions and lemon zest into mayonnaise mix. Lay courgettes out like soldiers onto a pre-heated shallow baking tray covered in baking paper. Neatly spoon 1-2 tsp of the breadcrumb mix thinly on top of each courgette slice. Carefully arrange sliced tomatoes on top, pop capers carefully in between the tomatoes and sprinkle them all with the parmesan. Squeeze the lemon and lime juice over them all. Bake in pre-heated 180C oven for 10-15 minutes and serve hot.

PRAWN & CHEESE CANAPÉS

This little Ayurvedic starter takes only minutes to make and is absolutely sensational to eat.
Served on rye bread, so is OK for those who avoid gluten.

serves 4

8 cooked jumbo king prawns	1 tsp yellow mustard seed
1 lime juice & zest	½ tsp cumin seeds
1 tbsp Boursin cheese	1 tsp Tabasco
2 tsp poppy seeds	1 tbsp chopped fresh coriander
6 chopped fresh chives	1 tsp chilli flakes
1 tbsp white/béchamel sauce	1 lemon
½ diced celery stick	black pepper
½ tsp turmeric	rye bread

Dry cook the mustard and cumin seeds until fragrant. Mix all the other ingredients
together in a mixing bowl, keeping some chives for garnish. Serve on toasted
rye bread cut into mini squares as canapés. Add remaining
chives on top for garnish.

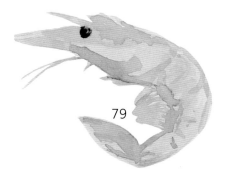

79

SALADS

Salads are a quick and easy way to combine the Ayurvedic six tastes, whilst eating mostly raw, healthy and nourishing food.

NIÇOISE SALAD

An Ayurvedic twist on this well-known and well-loved
French salad, originally from Nice

serves 4

1 cup diced black pitted olives	1 tbsp capers
1 tsp turmeric	½ tsp rock salt
2 tbsp white wine vinegar	1 bag leaf lettuce
1 handful fine green beans	3 hard boiled eggs cut into ¼'s
2 diced shallots	1 tbsp fresh chopped coriander
4 tbsp olive oil	1 tbsp fresh chopped oregano
1 cup diced baby plum tomatoes	1 lemon juice
2 tbsp Dijon mustard	1 bunch spring onions

Wash and chop lettuce and arrange in a large dish or bowl. Chop beans into one inch lengths and par-boil for two minutes. Arrange the green beans, olives, tomatoes, shallots, capers and eggs over the lettuce. Make the dressing by combining the lemon, salt, vinegar, Dijon mustard, oil and turmeric, and shaking together vigorously in an old jam jar or jug.
Sprinkle the herbs and spring onions across the salad.
Add the dressing immediately before serving.

WATERCRESS & PANCETTA SALAD

Watercress is grown all around us in Hampshire, and is native to both Europe and Asia. It is one of the oldest known leaf vegetables to be eaten by humans.

serves 4

1 tbsp soy sauce	1 tsp yellow mustard seeds
2 cups washed chopped spinach	2 tbsp diced pancetta lardons
2 tbsp sun-dried tomatoes	splash balsamic glaze
2 tbsp pine nuts	2 tbsp olive oil
1 bag washed watercress	1 lemon juice
1 cup fresh peas	black pepper
1 pinch cumin seeds	rock salt

Cook the diced lardons with cumin and mustard seeds. Coarsely chop the watercress and sun-dried tomatoes. Arrange spinach, tomatoes, pine nuts and peas in a salad bowl. Mix soy sauce, seasoning, lemon juice and olive oil together and drizzle over the salad with the balsamic glaze on top.

RADICCHIO & POMEGRANATE SALAD

This is a deliciously nutritious salad stuffed full of anthocyanins (from the red colour)
which are such great anti-oxidants for living younger longer.

serves 4

½ cup diced feta cheese	2 tbsp pine nuts
1 bag radicchio leaf salad	1 cup fresh peas
1 tbsp balsamic vinegar	1 cup fresh chopped coriander
1 cup pomegranate seeds	1 tbsp olive oil
1 bunch diced spring onions	1 squeezed lemon juice
½ diced cucumber	rock salt
1 bag washed chopped spinach	black pepper

Arrange and gently stir all the solid ingredients together in a salad bowl. Separately
mix the oil, vinegar, lemon juice and seasoning together and
drizzle over the salad.

ASPARAGUS, RADISH & GOATS CHEESE SALAD

This is a very English adaptation of my favourite Greek feta cheese salad. It tastes its best during the far too short English asparagus season.

serves 4

1 bunch radishes sliced	2 tbsp olive oil
1 bag radicchio leaf salad	1 cup broken up soft goats cheese
1 tbsp balsamic vinegar	squeeze of lime juice
1 bunch diced asparagus	1 tsp paprika
2 tbsp of chopped fresh mint	1 tsp yellow mustard seeds
1 diced cucumber	rock salt
1 tbsp lemon juice	black pepper

Separately par-boil/steam the asparagus for two minutes. Mix the oil, mustard seeds, seasoning, lemon and lime juice together with the vinegar. Mix all the salad ingredients together in a salad bowl and drizzle with the dressing.

TUNA & BEAN COUSCOUS SALAD

A Moroccan style salad with my
own Ayurvedic twist.

serves 4

¼ cup diced pitted black olives	2 tbsp sesame oil
1 tsp turmeric	1 jar shredded tuna
1 lemon juice	2 tbsp pine nuts
2 large diced courgettes	2 cups diced fine green beans
1 diced red onion	1 tsp paprika
2 tbsp sesame seeds	1 tsp yellow mustard seeds
3½ cups couscous	5 cups water
½ cup diced sun-dried tomatoes	2 cloves diced garlic
¼ cup capers	ground black pepper

Heat oil, add sesame, mustard seeds, garlic and onion, cook until soft, then add turmeric, beans, courgettes, tomatoes and stir continuously until al dente. Add pine nuts, capers, olives and tuna. Mix in couscous and add five cups boiling water. Take off the heat, to let couscous absorb the liquid. Serve with squeeze of lemon and paprika to taste.

SALMON, POMEGRANATE & PEA SALAD

A stunning looking salad to impress your guests, full of nutrients and takes only five minutes to prepare.

serves 4

1 bunch sliced radishes	1 tbsp pumpkin seeds
1 handful chopped chicory	1 tbsp sunflower seeds
2 lemons squeezed	1 tbsp sesame seeds
1 handful chopped romaine leaves	splash olive oil
1 bunch diced spring onions	balsamic vinegar
1 cup fresh peas	1 cup pomegranate seeds
½ diced cucumber	rock salt
1 slice cooked salmon flaked	cracked black pepper

Prepare the dressing by mixing the vinegar, seasoning, lemon juice and oil together. Gently arrange all the rest of the salad ingredients together in layers, finishing with radishes, seeds and pomegranate on top.
Drizzle with dressing.

MAIN MEALS

You will find that all these recipes are first prepared as freshly diced ingredients, then cooked briefly to retain all their natural vitamins and health benefits. Each recipe takes only 20-30 minutes to cook, which is ideal to preserve the energy and freshness of the nutritious ingredients.

CHICKEN & PRAWN PAELLA

A deliciously nutritious meal all year round. Created for my eldest daughter
who simply adores prawns in any shape or form!

serves 4

1 cup fresh/frozen king prawns	1 tsp smoked paprika
½ tsp turmeric	1 lemon juice
1 glass sherry vinegar	1 tsp dried rosemary
1 cup chopped fresh parsley	1 tsp dried basil
1 diced red onion	2 bay leaves
1 cup Arborio rice (200g)	1 pint veg stock
1 cup sliced cooked chicken	1 cup tomato puree
3 diced garlic cloves	5 diced sun-dried tomatoes
1 tsp yellow mustard seeds	1 diced red pepper
1 tbsp olive oil	1 cup frozen peas

Gently fry the prawns for five minutes until cooked, and put them aside. In the same pan, fry
the mustard seeds, onion, red pepper, sun-dried tomatoes and garlic together for five
minutes until softened. Add the turmeric and rest of herbs and spices, and stir well.
Add rice and vinegar keep stirring well to absorb the liquid. Add some of the veg stock,
cook and stir gently, and leave for 10 minutes to simmer. Then keep adding the rest
of the stock slowly, and leave to simmer and absorb all of the stock. Once rice is cooked,
stir in peas, prawns, chicken, and tomato puree, and warm them through.
Finally add the juice of a whole lemon and serve.

ARTICHOKE, RED ONION & CHICKPEA

*Fresh artichokes would be fantastic in this recipe but
are often so difficult to find.*

serves 4

1 tbsp soy sauce	1 tsp cardamom pods
1 tsp turmeric	2 cloves diced garlic
1 lemon juice	rock salt
1 jar antipasti artichokes	black pepper
1 diced red onion	1 tbsp olive oil
1 tbsp honey	1 tbsp sesame seeds
1 tsp yellow mustard seeds	1 tin cooked chickpeas
½ tsp cumin seeds	1 tin chopped tomatoes

Heat oil, add mustard, cumin, cardamom and sesame seeds. Cook for one minute.
Add the onion and garlic and cook for five minutes until soft. Add the turmeric, tomatoes,
artichokes, soy sauce, chickpeas, lemon juice, salt and pepper to taste. Then finally stir in
the honey and serve.

MUSHROOM RISOTTO

*The more exotic the variety of mushrooms you use
the better the flavour of this dish.*

serves 4-6

2 tbsp grated parmesan	3 cups diced mushrooms
1 tsp turmeric	2 tbsp olive oil
1 glass white wine	½ tsp cumin seeds
1 tbsp pine nuts	½ tsp coriander seeds
1 diced onion	1 lemon juice
1½ cups Arborio rice (300g)	1 lime juice
2 pints veg stock	rock salt
2 cloves diced garlic	black pepper

Cook rice in large pan with veg stock for 15-20 minutes with a pinch of salt, until al dente, then drain. Fry spices in a separate pan, with a splash of olive oil, for one minute until fragrant. Add garlic, onion and mushrooms, and cook until soft. Stir in turmeric, pine nuts, wine, lemon and lime juice. Season to taste. Mix with rice. Finally stir in parmesan and serve hot.

PEA & MINT RISOTTO

This was the last recipe I created for this book, as I had spotted some lovely fresh peas in their pods at the supermarket. It nearly didn't make it, but I am so glad it did, as the flavours are so deliciously summery. You really do taste the mint.

serves 4-6

2 tbsp freshly grated parmesan	1 tsp chilli flakes
1 tsp turmeric	1 tsp yellow mustard seeds
1 squeeze lemon juice	½ tsp cumin seeds
1 tbsp pine nuts	3 tbsp olive oil
2 cups fresh chopped mint (20g)	1 large glass white wine
3 mugs fresh/frozen peas	1 litre veg stock
1½ cups Arborio rice (300g)	1 squeeze lime juice
2 cloves diced garlic	rock salt
1 diced onion	black pepper

With a splash of the olive oil in a hot pan heat the mustard, pine nuts and cumin seeds for a minute, then add the garlic and onion and cook until soft. Stir in the turmeric, rice, wine, and chilli and heat for five minutes stirring all the time. Add a cupful of the stock and stir into the mix until all the liquid is absorbed. Repeat this until all the stock has been taken up by the rice, which should now be plump and soft. Add the rest of the olive oil.
Add lemon and lime juice and stir in the parmesan, peas and mint, stir for a few minutes and serve hot.
Season with salt and pepper.

ASPARAGUS, GINGER & PARMESAN RISOTTO

*This is an absolute scorcher for revving up your taste buds with the added 'superfood'
effect of ginger's natural anti-inflammatory properties.*

serves 4

2 tbsp parmesan cheese	3 tbsp olive oil
1 tsp turmeric	1 tsp yellow mustard seeds
1 glass white wine/cider/apple juice	½ tsp cumin seeds
2 cups diced asparagus	½ tsp coriander seeds
1 diced onion	1 litre water
1½ cups of Arborio rice	2 tbsp diced fresh ginger
2 diced garlic cloves	black pepper

Fry the mustard, cumin and coriander seeds in a pan with a splash of the olive oil to release
their aromatics. Add the onion, ginger and garlic and cook until soft. Add rice and sauté
for three minutes. Add the wine and turmeric and stir for one minute. Add water
bit-by-bit, still gently stirring over heat, until all of it is absorbed by the rice. Finally
when al dente, add the parmesan, pepper and a small dash of
olive oil, to create a shine, and serve.

AYURVEDIC CAULIFLOWER CHEESE

Cauliflowers are great as they are so solid, that you can actually bake a whole cauliflower, and pour the cheese mix on top for a crowd-pleaser.

serves 4

2 tbsp grated cheese	1 tsp mustard seeds
1 tsp fenugreek	1 tsp cardamom pods
1 lemon juice and zest	½ tsp coriander seeds
1 diced cauliflower	1 tsp turmeric
1 diced onion	1 tsp whole grain mustard
½ pint béchamel/white sauce	1 tbsp Tabasco
1 tbsp olive oil	rock salt
½ tsp cumin seeds	black pepper

Stir fry the mustard, cumin, fenugreek, coriander seeds and cardamom pods in a splash of oil to release their aromatics. Add the onion and cook until soft. Meanwhile blanch the cauliflower in a separate pan of salted boiling water until al dente. Then mix cauliflower with the spices and add the béchamel sauce, cheese, Tabasco, lemon juice and zest and turmeric. Season to taste. Bake in a pre-heated 180C oven for 15 minutes.

FAMILY FISH PIE

A deliciously filling family favourite which satiates everyone.
Extremely easy to make.

serves 4

12 jumbo fresh/frozen prawns	1 tsp yellow mustard seeds
1 cup chopped spinach	1 cup sweetcorn
8 sliced cherry tomatoes	1 cup fresh/frozen peas
4 cups mashed potato	1 tbsp tarragon
1 red onion	1 tbsp Tabasco
1 cup diced carrots	black pepper
2 cups cod/haddock in 1 inch cubes	1 tbsp turmeric
2 cloves diced garlic	½ tsp cumin seeds
2 hard boiled eggs in quarters	½ tsp coriander seeds
3 tbsp grated cheese	olive oil
1 lemon juice	rock salt

Fry mustard, cumin and coriander seeds in a splash of oil. Add onion, carrots and garlic and cook until soft. Add prawns and fish and stir in well. Mix all into mashed potato. Add sweetcorn, peas, tarragon, Tabasco, turmeric and spinach. Carefully stir in eggs and lemon juice and season to taste. Spoon the mix into an oven proof dish, decorate with tomatoes on top and sprinkle parmesan all over. Bake in pre-heated 200C oven for 30-40 minutes.

ROCKET & CORIANDER OMELETTE

A simple nutritious Ayurvedic breakfast or as a
main meal any time of the day.

generously serves 2

rock salt	**splash milk**
1 cup coarsely chopped rocket	6 small or 5 medium eggs
1 lemon juice	½tsp yellow mustard seeds
1 cup coarsely chopped fresh coriander	1 tbsp olive oil
1 diced onion	black pepper

Beat eggs and milk in a bowl with salt and pepper to taste. Put aside. Heat oil and add
yellow mustard seeds and onion and stir on medium heat. Allow to sweat together until
onions are soft. Add rocket and stir for 30 seconds, then coriander and cook for 15 seconds.
Pour on egg mix, still on medium heat, until it bubbles. Ease uncooked egg from around the
edges into the centre of the pan, folding it gently to cook it all to a soft omelette consistency.
Serve on toasted rye bread with squeeze of lemon juice.

ROCKET & SCALLOP BAKE

Scallops are high in magnesium and full of protein and provide a heavenly texture as well as being one of the significant six tastes in this dish.

serves 4

8 scallops	1 cup frozen/fresh peas
1 bag rocket	3 cups spinach
8 sliced cherry tomatoes	1 lime juice
1 cup diced sweet potatoes	1 chopped chicory
2 cloves diced garlic	1 tsp yellow mustard seeds
1 cup sweetcorn	½ tsp cumin seeds
1 tsp turmeric	½ lemon juice
2 tbsp parmesan	seasoning

Fry mustard and cumin seeds until popping. Add garlic and sweet potatoes and stir until soft. Add chicory and turmeric, and when soft add spinach, lemon and lime juice. In a baking dish, layer sweet potato mix, then a layer of scallops and tomatoes, and finally a layer of rocket and cheese. Bake at 190C for 15 minutes.

COURGETTE STIR FRY

A lovely summery dish with Ayurvedic
flavours for added pizazz.

serves 2-4

1 cup diced celery	1 lemon juice & zest
1 tsp turmeric	2 tsp sesame seeds
½ cup yoghurt	3 cloves diced garlic
3 diced courgettes	2 diced tomatoes
1 diced onion	½ tsp coriander seeds
½ diced cucumber	1 tsp yellow mustard seeds
1 tbsp olive oil	black pepper
½ tsp cumin seeds	rock salt

Heat oil and add mustard, coriander and cumin seeds and stir until popping. Add celery, courgettes, onions, garlic and tomatoes and cook until soft. Add turmeric, lemon, and sesame seeds and stir until soft. Turn down heat and season to taste.
Finally stir in yoghurt.

HAM & CHICORY BAKE

I was first shown this recipe on an organic Welsh farm in my old M&S days. They served it to me on a large mirror! I have loved the combination of chicory and ham ever since and have now adapted it into an Ayurvedic dish.

serves 4

2 slices ham	1 cucumber
2 chicory bulbs	1 lemon juice
½ cup grated Gruyère cheese	½ tsp turmeric
1 tbsp poppy seeds	1 tbsp chopped fresh oregano
1 tbsp chopped chives	seasoning

Mix the cheese, turmeric, poppy seeds, chives, oregano and seasoning together in a small bowl. Slice the chicory bulbs in half longitudinally, leaving the stalk end intact.
Slice the cucumber longitudinally into approximately 3mm thick slices. Heat oven to 180C.
Place the chicory pieces on a baking tray, cut side facing upwards. Layer a cucumber slice on top of each chicory piece then place the ham as a layer on top. Finally add the cheese mix on top of it all and squeeze the lemon juice over it all. Bake in the oven for 15 minutes until the cheese has turned golden brown.
Serve hot.

CHICKEN & ASPARAGUS MASH

*This recipe is a great way to use up left-overs. Use left-over boiled/mashed
potatoes and left-over chicken or turkey.*

serves 4

1 diced celery stick	2 tbsp diced mushrooms
1 tsp turmeric	1 tsp paprika
1 lemon juice	1 tbsp dried tarragon
1 cup diced asparagus	1 tbsp sesame seeds
½ red onion diced	½ tsp cumin seeds
1 tsp honey	1 tsp yellow mustard seeds
3 cups mashed potato	1 tbsp pine nuts
2 tbsp diced cooked turkey/chicken	1 tbsp Tabasco sauce
1 tbsp olive oil	black pepper

Steam the asparagus until al dente. Meanwhile heat a little oil in a frying pan, and cook
mustard, sesame and cumin seeds until fragrant. Add the asparagus, red onion, celery
and mushrooms. Cook until soft. Add the chicken and tarragon and stir in for 5-10 minutes.
Add the potato to the chicken mix and stir in gently. Mix separately the Tabasco, turmeric,
honey and lemon juice, add to the chicken mash and sprinkle with pine nuts
(toasted if desired) and paprika. Season to taste and
serve piping hot.

FAVOURITE APPLE & CHICKEN DISH

A clean nutritious balance of flavours, which feels satisfyingly healthy and filling. As long as you use the colour coded ingredients, you don't have to use ALL the rest. Just use whatever takes your fancy.

serves 4

1 cup lardons (remove fat)	1 lime juice
1 tsp turmeric	1 tbsp sesame seeds
1 cup diced tomatoes	½ tsp cumin seeds
2 cups diced apple	½ tsp yellow mustard seeds
2 cloves diced garlic	½ tsp coriander seeds
2 cups diced chicken	2 tbsp grated parmesan
½ cup chopped walnuts	1 tbsp dried/fresh tarragon
1 tbsp chopped almonds	1 tbsp fresh/dried oregano
1 cup diced courgettes	1 tbsp freshly chopped rosemary
1 cup diced celery stalk	2 lemons squeezed
1 cup diced broccoli	olive oil
1 diced red onion	black pepper

Add a splash of olive oil to a hot pan with onion, garlic, mustard, cumin and coriander seeds. Stir well until onion and garlic are soft. Add a splash of water to loosen the ingredients. Add sesame seeds and mix the flavours. Add the lardons, turmeric and broccoli. Add chicken, rosemary, oregano and stir until cooked. Add the courgettes, celery and tomatoes and a splash of water to keep them moist. Keep stirring to cook. Add apple, tarragon, walnuts and squeezed lemon and lime juice to the mix. Season with black pepper. Mix in almonds and parmesan, stir well and serve.

MUSHROOM STIR FRY

*Our family can't get enough mushrooms, especially our youngest
daughter, so this recipe was created for her.*

serves 4

1 tbsp soy sauce	1 tbsp white wine vinegar
1 tsp turmeric	1 tbsp sesame seeds
1 lemon juice	½ tsp cumin seeds
1 cup chopped green beans	½ tsp yellow mustard seeds
1 tbsp diced fresh ginger	½ tsp coriander seeds
2 medium sliced carrots	1 tbsp chopped fresh coriander
1 diced red pepper	1 lime juice
2 cups chopped mushrooms	seasoning to taste

Heat a little oil in a pan over a medium heat. Cook sesame, mustard, cumin and coriander
seeds until fragrant and popping. Add the rest of the ingredients except lemon, lime and fresh
coriander to the pan and stir fry, adding occasional splashes of water (splash at a time)
as necessary to prevent the mixture sticking. Stir fry for 10-15 minutes until all ingredients
are cooked and tender. Drizzle with lemon and lime juice.
Garnish with fresh coriander.

PRAWN & CELERY COUSCOUS

My husband is an excellent cook, and especially good at his homemade couscous dishes. This is based on one of his dishes with my Ayurvedic adjustments.

serves 4

1 cup king prawns	1 tbsp dry/fresh chopped oregano
½ **sliced chicory**	1 tsp yellow mustard seeds
1 lemon juice	½ tsp cumin seeds
1 cup diced asparagus	½ tsp coriander seeds
1 diced red onion	1 tbsp soy sauce
1 cup diced carrots	1 tsp turmeric
2 diced garlic cloves	½ cup couscous
1 sliced celery stick	1 cup veg stock
2 tsp olive oil	black pepper
1 cup chopped parsley	rock salt

Fry spices in a pan with a splash of olive oil. Add garlic, onion, carrots, celery and chicory and stir for 5-10 minutes until soft. Then add asparagus, soy sauce, prawns and turmeric. Stir on medium heat, and put a lid on the pan to let it all soften. Add couscous and mix it up to absorb the flavours and juices. Add a cupful of boiling veg stock to the mix, gently fold in, put the lid back on and leave to cook for five minutes. Serve with a squeeze of lemon juice, parsley and seasoning.

LENTILS & LARDONS

*A scrumptious, healthy favourite, especially welcome
on cold winter nights.*

serves 4

1 handful smoked lardons	1 tsp yellow mustard seeds
½ diced chicory	½ tsp cumin seeds
1 lemon juice	½ tsp coriander seeds
1 tin of cooked lentils	1 tsp turmeric
1 small diced onion	1 tbsp chopped thyme
1 small diced carrot	1 lime juice
½ stick diced celery	2 tbsp olive oil
2 cloves chopped garlic	rock salt
1 tbsp pre-soaked almonds	black pepper

Fry the mustard, cumin and coriander seeds on medium heat. Add lardons until lightly browned. In the same pan add the onion, carrot, almonds, celery, chicory, and garlic (scraping up all the sticky bits from the bottom of the pan) for a few minutes until soft and the onions are translucent. Add the turmeric and stir for one minute with the lemon and lime juice. Add lentils, stir for five minutes on medium heat, and season to taste.

SWEET POTATO, CRANBERRIES & RED ONION

I absolutely adore all potatoes as my family will testify. However, with my Ayurvedic hat on, I realise how great sweet potatoes are for you, and they can do almost everything a standard spud can.

serves 4

½ diced celery	2 cups tinned tomatoes/passata
1 cup dried/fresh cranberries	1 tsp turmeric
1 lemon juice and zest	1 tbsp cup freshly grated ginger
1 diced cooked sweet potato	1 tbsp flaked almonds
1 diced red onion	1 pint veg stock
2 tbsp honey	1 tin cooked chickpeas
olive oil	1 bunch chopped coriander
1 tsp yellow mustard seeds	rock salt
½ tsp cumin seeds	black pepper

Heat one tbsp oil in a pan and add mustard and cumin seeds. Add onions, celery and sweet potato and cook until soft. Add turmeric, ginger, honey, passata and cranberries, bring to boil. Reduce the heat, cover, simmer for 10 minutes. Add more water if the mixture is too thick. Meanwhile, in a separate pan, add chickpeas, lemon zest and veg stock and stir briefly. Leave for five minutes. Add lemon juice, almonds and splash of oil and add to mix. Serve altogether with a sprinkling of fresh coriander and season to taste.

AYURVEDIC CHRISTMAS MEAL

A great alternative to the traditional Christmas meal, which you can make completely vegetarian by taking out the turkey and lardons. If so, use a cup of diced celery or radishes to replace the 'salty' taste of substituted lardons. Otherwise it is great for left-over turkey, after your main Christmas meal.

serves 4

1 cup bacon lardons	1 tbsp oregano
1 tsp turmeric	½ tsp cumin
1 cup cranberries	1 tsp yellow mustard seeds
1 cup diced green beans	½ tsp coriander seeds
1 diced red onion	3 fresh chives
1 tbsp pine nuts	1 tbsp fresh chopped coriander
2 diced garlic cloves	1 tbsp Tabasco
1 cup sun-dried tomatoes	1 cup diced cherry tomatoes
2 cups cooked diced turkey	olive oil
1 tin red lentils	2 tbsp parmesan
1 cup cooked potato cubes	rock salt
1 lemon juice	black pepper

Heat a splash of oil in a pan. Add mustard, coriander and cumin seeds. When popping, add garlic and onion and cook until soft. Add lardons, green beans, turmeric and potato. Keep stirring, and mix flavours with a dash of water. Add pine nuts, oregano, and cranberries. Stir for another minute and add lentils, lemon, turkey, Tabasco and tomatoes until cooked. Add parmesan and fresh coriander, season to taste. Decorate with chives and serve.

SCALLOPS & GRAPE LENTIL MIX

*A typical Ayurvedic technique of introducing fruit into a savoury dish
for an explosion of flavour on your tongue.*

serves 4

4-6 large scallops	black pepper
1 tsp turmeric	olive oil
8 sliced cherry tomatoes	1 tbsp fresh diced ginger
5 broccoli florets	1 tsp yellow mustard seeds
1 sliced leek	½ tsp cumin seeds
8 halved seedless grapes	1 tsp tarragon
2 tbsp pre-cooked red lentils	1 tsp coriander powder
2 tbsp white wine	1 tsp Tabasco
1 lemon juice	2 chopped chives

Boil pan of water, par-boil broccoli two minutes. Separately heat one tbsp oil in pan and cook mustard and cumin seeds until popping. Add leek and ginger and stir until soft. Turn down heat, add tomatoes, broccoli, lentils, turmeric, coriander powder, tarragon, white wine, black pepper and lemon juice. Separately fry scallops in a splash of oil with Tabasco.
Mix all together and garnish with chives.

PUDDINGS

I have only included two recipes in this section, mainly because puddings aren't that big in Ayurvedic cooking.

MACEDONIA FRUIT SALAD

Inspired by a short summer stay with an eccentric grand old lady in Sardinia, who introduced me to a version of this recipe, as well as her belief that she had made some natural plant/herbal cures for cancer.

serves 4

3 diced black pitted olives	12 diced seedless grapes
1 orange rind and juice	3 diced nectarines
1 lemon juice	2 diced apples
2 tbsp pomegranate seeds	8-10 dried/fresh apricots
1 sprig fresh mint	2 tbsp honey
1 tbsp chopped almonds	2 tbsp soft dark brown sugar
3 diced kiwis	½ cup water

Make the apricot sauce, by melting the sugar, honey, water, lemon and orange juice together in a pan. When melted add the apricots and stir on high heat and keep gently stirring until the apricots have become completely pulpy and soft. Allow to cool. Mix all the remaining ingredients together in a separate bowl. Serve with the apricot sauce and some mint on top for garnish.

UDDA PUDDA

Our family's favourite chocolate pudding. It is quite rich and strong, so you only need to serve a small amount to each person. Its intense flavour makes it almost like a non-alcoholic chocolate shot!

serves 4-6

3 pitted black olives	**1 tbsp honey**
1 tbsp cacao	6 chopped dates
Splash of orange juice	2 tbsp greek yoghurt
½ punnet blueberries	1 tbsp coconut oil
fresh mint	1 zest orange

Whizz all together for 30 seconds in blender and serve garnished with a sprig of fresh mint.

APPENDIX

DOSHA TYPES

When your doshas become unbalanced (due to ill health, medicines, poor eating habits, not enough exercise etc.) it can lead to major health problems. There are three doshas:

Vata – Dry skin, cold, light, irregular

When your vata is balanced it is cool, calm and collected. If it is out of balance it becomes chaotic, anxious, it causes irregular breathing, coughs, hiccups, erratic movements in the intestines and the circulation, causing erratic heartbeats and cold extremities.

- You don't like cold weather, don't gain weight easily. You have a thin body frame, often become anxious and restless, moods changing quickly.
- You are creative and imaginative, are active, fidgety, walk quickly, have difficulty falling or staying asleep.
- You tend to have dry, rough skin especially in winter, dry, thin, dark, curly, hair and cold feet and hands.
- You make friends easily and quickly change them. Under stress, easily excited, learn quickly but forget quickly.
- You have an irregular appetite. You are very energetic, with low endurance and stamina.
- You have a good short-term memory, poor long term memory.
- You have small, sunken, brown roving eyes, sharp pointed irregular nose with narrow long thin nostrils.

Pitta – oily skin, warm, intense

When pitta is balanced it is passionate, energetic and patient. Out of balance pitta
becomes a volcano burning everything in its path, becoming harshly critical of itself
or others, its natural decision-making processes become reduced, inflaming digestive
processes, leading to ulcers and bleeding, high body temperature, hyper-metabolism, and
red or flushed skin.

- You don't like hot weather, have average weight for your build, medium body
  frame, often become intense and irritable, moods are intense and slow to change.
- You are intelligent, efficient and a perfectionist, sharp, fast, clear and critical,
  have a determined walk, sleep well for an average length of time.
- You tend to have moist warm, smooth, oily, rosy, or freckled skin, and oily, straight,
  blonde, red, grey or balding hair.
- Most of your friends are work-related. Under stress you are easily angered
  and critical.
- You are moderately energetic and have a tendency to overheat. You are
  uncomfortable missing meals, and like cold drinks and food.
- You have a good critical memory.
- Your eyes are light blue/hazel, or green, sharp and light sensitive. You have a
  straight Roman nose.

Kapha – moist cool skin, heavy, solid

A balanced kapha is strong and supportive, giving emotional and physical strength to whatever they commit to doing. However when excessive, the lungs and digestive system can become congested, leading to difficulty breathing and poor digestion, a tendency to put on weight, and mobility can become restricted.

- You don't like damp cool weather, have a heavy, solid, large body-frame, gain weight easily.
- You can be slow or depressed, and moods are mostly steady, with a calm, steady, stable mind, can be stubborn and not easily ruffled.
- You have good long-term memory and your friendships are long-lasting and sincere.
- You have a steady slow walk and sleep long and soundly.
- You can skip meals easily, and eat and digest slowly.
- You have good stamina and a steady energy level.
- You tend to have soft, cool, wet, thick, pale skin with oily lustrous thick wavy brown hair, large brown, or blue steady eyes, and large, wide nostrils.

DOSHA QUESTIONNAIRE

In order to find out which dosha type you are, ideally you would need to be assessed by an Ayurvedic doctor. They will check your temperature, pressure points and tongue, amongst other tests, to assess which is your most dominant dosha and how balanced/ imbalanced it is.

However, by ticking all of the boxes in these three questionnaires which apply to you, you can establish very quickly which dosha type you are most likely to be.
The dosha type with the highest score applies to you.

Vata Questionnaire

1. Are you best described as underweight to slim? ☐
2. Do you have a slender or fine-boned figure? ☐
3. Do you have dry, thin, dark or curly hair? ☐
4. Do you have fine, small and cool hands? ☐
5. Are your finger nails rather thin and elongated? ☐
6. Do you have a predisposition to dry or rough skin? ☐
7. Do you perspire minimally or only under heavy exertion? ☐
8. Do you tend to jump erratically from one thought to the next? ☐
9. Is your short-term memory better than your long-term memory? ☐
10. Under pressure, do you tend to be hectic or exhibit stress reactions? ☐
11. Is it generally difficult for you to make decisions? ☐
12. Are you interested in many things, and do you gladly absorb new information? ☐
13. Are you imaginative and creative? ☐
14. Do you tend toward a very flexible, sometimes unsteady lifestyle? ☐
15. Is there a tendency toward irregular and often hard bowel movements? ☐
16. Do you become cold easily, and do you prefer a warm climate? ☐
17. Are irregular times for eating meals unproblematic for you? ☐
18. Do you have a changeable appetite? ☐
19. Do you have a tendency towards flatulence or bloating? ☐
20. Are you full of drive, but become tired quickly? ☐

Pitta Questionnaire

1. Are you of average weight? ☐

2. Is your musculature well developed? ☐

3. Does your hair tend toward fine, silky or reddish, or is it prematurely grey or showing signs of hair loss? ☐

4. Do you have warm, rosy and well formed hands? ☐

5. Are your fingernails thin, elastic and pink coloured? ☐

6. Does your skin have beauty spots, freckles or an oily tendency? ☐

7. Do you tend to emit strong body odour when perspiring? ☐

8. Is your pattern of thinking precise and logical? ☐

9. Do you generally have a good memory? ☐

10. Are you frequently impatient, irritable or irate? ☐

11. Do you have a strong will and a good talent for organisation? ☐

12. Do you work quickly and accurately by nature? ☐

13. Do you tend toward perfectionism, and do you put yourself under pressure to perform? ☐

14. Do you have a well organised lifestyle? ☐

15. Do you have regular stools or a softer bowel movement more than once a day? ☐

16. Are you uncomfortable in hot weather and do you prefer a cooler climate? ☐

17. Do you get angry or in a bad mood if an expected meal is missed or delayed? ☐

18. Can you eat what you want, and do you tolerate heavy food? ☐

19. Do you tend towards skin flushes, infections and inflammations of any kind? ☐

20. Do you have an average amount of energy? ☐

Kapha Questionnaire

1. Are you more of a steady type, and do you easily gain weight? ☐
2. Do you have a stocky figure? ☐
3. Do you have thick, full hair? ☐
4. Are your hands large, calm and strong? ☐
5. Do you have strong, even and broad fingernails? ☐
6. Is your skin firm, pure and light-coloured? ☐
7. Do perspire constantly, even without exertion? ☐
8. Is your mode of thought calm and deliberate? ☐
9. Do you have good short-term and long-term memory? ☐
10. Do you tend to be clingy and possessive? ☐
11. Is it difficult to make you lose your composure? ☐
12. Are you often tired, lethargic or unmotivated? ☐
13. Are you not especially ambitious, but more often lackadaisical? ☐
14. Do you have a steady lifestyle? ☐
15. Do you tend toward a large quantity of and solid bowel movements? ☐
16. Do you feel uncomfortable in wet or damp environments or at high altitudes? ☐
17. Is it easy for you to miss a meal? ☐
18. Do you have a moderate appetite, and do you savour good food? ☐
19. Do you tend towards colds, hay fever or asthma? ☐
20. Do you have a high energy and plenty of stamina? ☐

SUPERFOODS

Green tea – lowers cardiovascular risks, lowers blood pressure, lowers carbohydrate and fat absorption

Soy sauce – improves bone health and blood lipid profile

Mushrooms – anti-carcinogen, immune-regulator, reduces cholesterol

Black rice – (not to be confused with white rice mixed with squid ink as used in some French restaurants) reduces weight, BMI, body fat, and reduces risk of coronary heart disease

Seaweed – cuts absorption of fat, speeds weight loss

Turmeric – keeps heart, brain and joints healthy. An anti-carcinogen, antiseptic and anti-inflammatory both internally and externally

Red wine – boosts brainpower, keeps heart healthy

Tomato puree – helps to maintain healthy blood flow and benefits circulation

Fruit – improves immunity, improves mental performance, satiety and anti-oxidants

Oats – improve satiation, reduces cholesterol and LDL, improves immune stimulation

Yellow mustard seeds – reduce diabetes, colon cancer, cholesterol, glucose levels, and acts as an anti-carcinogen in the gut

Seafood/fish – lowers blood pressure, improves visual activity, reduces chance of dementia and general cognitive decline in old age, benefits the brain of babies if taken in last stages of pregnancy*

Blueberries – protect against cancer and fights the sticky protein behind Alzheimer's disease

Chilli – eases pain, prevents stomach ulcers and speeds up metabolism

Spinach – speeds recovery after heart attack

Dark chocolate – reduces stress and cuts risk of heart disease

Beetroot juice – boosts stamina, lowers blood pressure

Honey – improves memory, cuts anxiety and kills germs

Garlic – improves performance of antibiotics, a natural antibiotic, anti-inflammatory and antiseptic. Improves heart health

Quinoa – regulates blood sugar, anti-inflammatory, good for energy and body metabolism as well as bones and muscles

Pine nuts – appetite suppressant

* *'Palaeontologists believe that some pre-historic men went to the beach and ate fish, and their brains grew. They got off all fours, walked and went back to the beach and became more intelligent than the others. Fish increases brain function in humans.'*
(Functional Food Conference, Oxford, 2012)

'Fats and carbs have a synergistic effect'

'Proteins and carbs have an antagonistic effect'

'The future will all be about tailored nutrition, and to design food to go to the right place. Smart delivery of food to the right place in the body quickly has a systematic effect on the whole body'

'There are many bioactives in plants that naturally reduce the risk of degenerative diseases, improve longevity, and reduce dependence on medicines'

REFERENCES

An introduction to Ayurveda Pukka Herbs Ltd

Ayurveda, remedies and inspirations for well-being Dr Donn Brennan

The quick and easy ayurvedic cookbook Eileen Keavy-Smith

The complete book of ayurvedic home remedies – a comprehensive guide to the ancient healing of India Vasant Lad

Gut. The Inside Story of our body's most underrated organ Guilia Enders

Oxford International Functional food Conference papers

The Diet Myth Professor Tim Spector

Abstracts from 1st UK International Functional Food Conference, Oxford 2012

INDEX

SOUR

PUNGENT

ASTRINGENT

SWEET

BITTER

SALTY